Levels 3-4

Reading Skills Activity Book

This book belongs to ...

....

Written by Kate Ruttle, based on the
original characters created by Roderick
Hunt and Alex Brychta

OXFORD
UNIVERSITY PRESS

colour the tails

Finish the pattern to colour the kites' tails.
Draw a picture on the kites to decorate them.

Finish the picture

Draw the patterns on Kipper's t-shirt and Wilma's hat.

Why? Completing patterns improves pencil control which is important for clear handwriting.

What did Biff do?

Choose the best sentence for each picture. Write the sentence under the picture.

Biff fell down.   Biff looked at the stump.

Biff pulled on the rope.   Biff looked at Mum and Dad.

....

....

4

Why? Children need to be able to read simple sentences and show their understanding by matching them to the images. Copying the sentence will practise handwriting and spelling.

Biff helps out!

Read the story together. Find the stickers of Biff, Dad and the stump to finish the pictures.

"That old tree stump has to go," said Dad.

"When I say pull, pULL!" said Dad.

Why? Predicting or remembering what happened next is an important comprehension skill that children should practise.

"When I shout pull, PULL!" said Dad.

"When I yell pull, pULL!" said Dad.

What do you think happened next?

Does this story remind you of another story you know?

This story is like the traditional tale 'The Enormous Turnip.'

Who's winning?

Use the stickers to finish the picture.
Who's winning the raft race?
Who will come last?

Levels 3-4 Reading Skills Activity Book

Stickers for pages 6 and 7

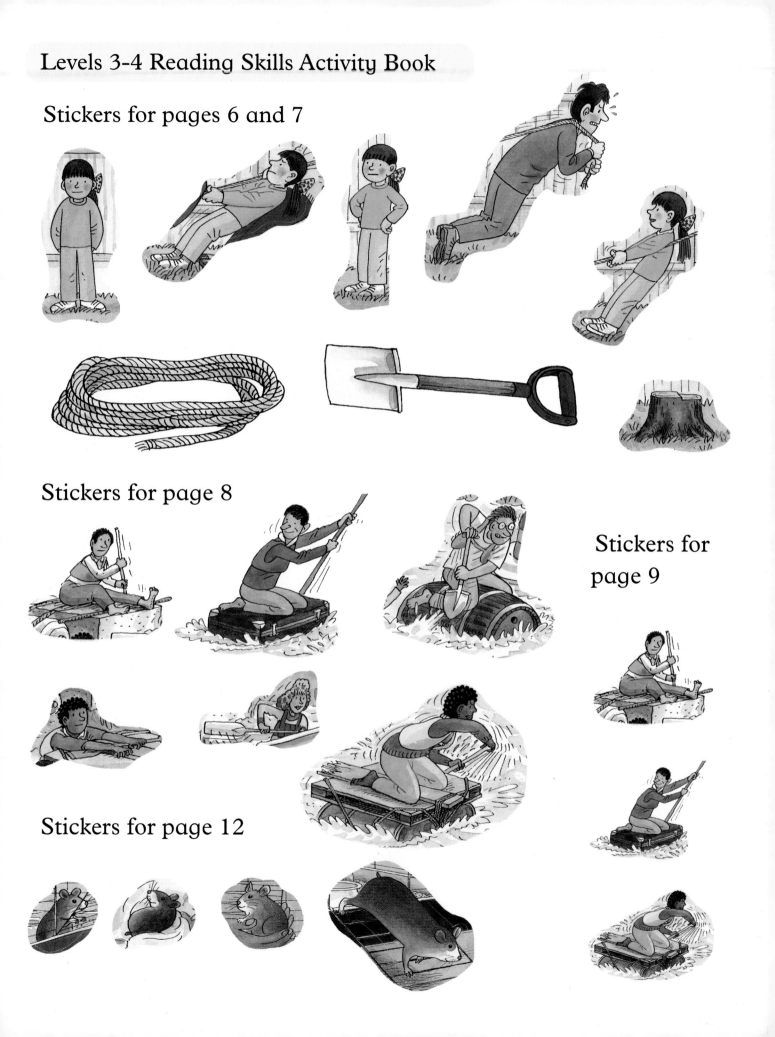

Stickers for page 8

Stickers for page 9

Stickers for page 12

Who's who?

Match the clothes and colours people are wearing to find out who is who.

Who is it?

Use the information to work out which stickers should go in the boxes.

Why? Attention to detail is key to sucessful reading.

What's missing?

Fill in the missing letters.
One label is done for you.

s.pots

ba____h

sp____ash

st____ipe

s____ade

g____ass

Wi____f

Why? In order for children to read successfully they need to be able to read and write words which contain adjacent consonants.

Missing?

Jaws is missing from these pictures.
Can you find him?

Nadim had a hamster
called Jaws.

Nadim forgot to
shut the cage door.

Jaws ran away.

Use the stickers to finish the pictures.

Can you see Jaws?

Where is Jaws?

Write the word to say what is happening in each picture.

out   down   under   in

Jaws got .... of his cage.

Jaws went .... his ladder.

Chip looked .... the sofa.

Chip looked .... the fridge.

Dad looked .... the floorboards.

Floppy looked .... the basket.

Why? Selecting the correct missing word indicates that children have fully understood the sentence. Copying words accurately is good handwriting practice.

13

Match the bugs!

Draw lines to join each pair of bugs.

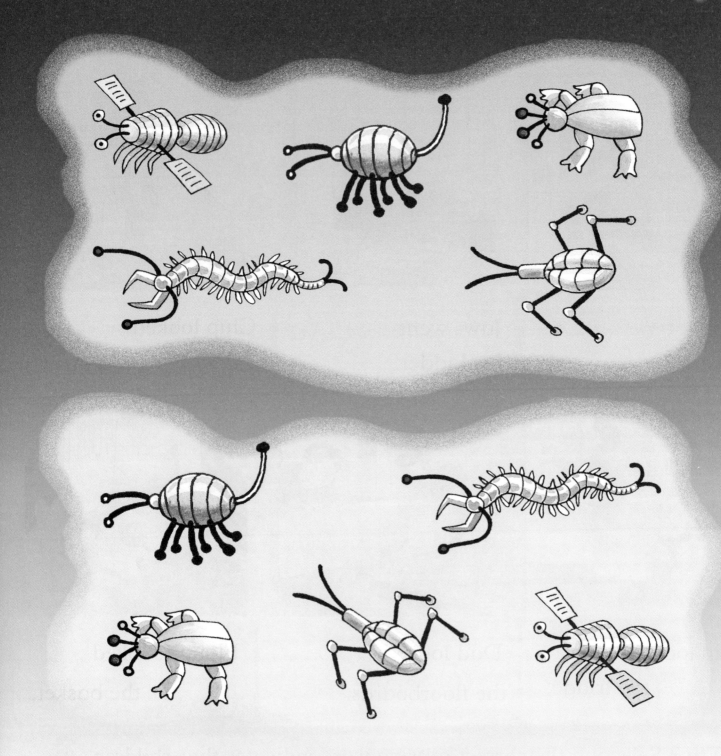

Why? Recognising details is an important skill for reading and writing.

Draw a bug!

Draw your own space bug!

Why? Creativity and independent thinking are particularly important for writing and can be practised through drawing and storytelling.

Rhyming words

Draw lines to match the words and pictures.
Circle the rhyming pairs of words.

nest	jump
rest	bump
space	sand
race	hand
egg	pet
leg	wet

Why? Hearing rhymes and using rhyming words to work out spelling patterns are important skills for reading and spelling.

OXFORD
UNIVERSITY PRESS

Great Clarendon Street, Oxford OX2 6DP

Text © Kate Ruttle 2006

Illustrations © Alex Brychta 2006

The characters in this work are the original creation of Roderick Hunt and Alex Brychta who retain copyright in the characters.

First Published 2006
This edition published 2013
All rights reserved

British Library Cataloguing in Publication Data available

ISBN 978-0-19-273484-6
Printed in India